CORBYN
THE RESURRECTION

And the Angel came in unto her, and said,
'Hail, thou art highly favoured, the Roop is with thee,
Blessed art thou among women.
And, behold thou shalt bring forth a son,
And shalt call his name Jeremiah
Who shall be easy meat hereafter.'

FOR HEATHER

CORBYN
THE RESURRECTION

STEVE BELL

First published by Guardian Faber in 2018

Guardian Faber is an imprint of Faber & Faber Ltd,
Bloomsbury House, 74–77 Great Russell Street,
London WC1B 3DA

Guardian is a registered trade mark of
Guardian News & Media Ltd,
Kings Place, 90 York Way, London N1 9GU

Printed in Europe

A CIP record for this book
is available from the British Library

ISBN 978–1–783–35160–2

2 4 6 8 10 9 7 5 3 1

THE BEGINNING OF THE GOSPEL OF JEREMIAH,
AS IT IS WRITTEN . . .

Ed the Batshit appeared in the wilderness, preaching a baptism of moderate austerity for the forgiveness of energy bills and controls on immigration.

Now Ed was clothed in camel's hair, and ate bacon in a sandwich. And he preached, saying,

'After me comes He who is mightier than I, the thong of whose sandals and the thread of whose red socks I am not worthy to stoop down and unravel. I have baptised you with water, but He will baptise you with the Strong Tea of Raw Socialism.'

In those days Jeremiah came from Shropshire by way of Islington. And when He came up out of the water, immediately He saw the heavens opened and the Rupert descending upon him like a heavily armed dove; and a voice came from heaven, 'I read in my beloved *Sun* that thou art the Holy Terror, off with whom I am well pissed.'

THE AWAKENING CONSCIENCE

'What would happen if somebody ever came to power that
you actually agreed with?'

Not a question that troubles most people, but spare a thought for the left-wing satirist, used to lacerating Tory, Labour and coalition governments with equal ferocity. Yet while I am sometimes asked this question at the end of talks or presentations, so far has any one party – in government or in opposition – ever been from representing my own views that it has always remained largely academic. Until today.

How on earth can I attack Jeremy Corbyn when I find myself agreeing with most of what he says? Political cartooning is an offensive, attacking medium or it is nothing. The prospect of a 'positive' political cartoon is more than faintly nauseating, for the practitioner as much as for the viewer.

T here are regrettably still places on earth where one can be assaulted, imprisoned or even murdered for caricaturing someone in power. But here, where our tradition of cruel, foul and personal abuse of those in power is, like Andrex, both long and strong, the worst thing for any self-respecting savage cartoonist would be for their victim to actually enjoy it.

Some politicians do actually revel in the amount of attention required to caricature them, let alone the infinitely greater effort needed to turn them into a viable cartoon character. But because the pointed intention to wound is invariably there, most politicians maintain a dignified silence in response to such treatment. Very rarely do they allow you the satisfaction of letting you know that you have got to them.

One such rarity was John Prescott. Once the last hope of the left of the Labour party, he lost heavily to the young, vibrant and charismatic right-winger Tony Blair in the leadership election of 1994. He then allowed himself to be co-opted into the grand New Labour project to dig up the embalmed corpse of socialism, freeze-dry it, shatter it, grind it into dust and then bury it again. Or, to put it more simply, to abolish Clause Four of the Labour party constitution and its commitment to:

. . . the common ownership of the means of production, distribution and exchange, and the best obtainable system of popular administration and control of each industry or service.

Prescott let it be known in the strongest possible terms that he objected to being depicted as a neutered dog with the miraculous ability to recite the new Clause Four from memory backwards.

Now, twenty-one years later, having been elevated to the cushioned splendour of the House of Lords while Blair pursues a lucrative career outside of parliament as businessman and peace envoy, Baron Prescott of Kingston upon Hull has suddenly turned on his former master. What on earth could have brought about such a transformation? It could only be the Corbyn effect

CORBYN

YOU HAVE MADE THE LABOUR PARTY COMPLETELY UNELECTABLE

Some faces lend themselves readily to caricature and Jeremy Corbyn's is a good example. Where Margaret Thatcher had a staring (some would say 'mad') left eye and a hooded right eye, and where Tony Blair has a mad/staring left eye and a smiley, twinkly right eye, Corbyn has a mad/staring right eye and a hooded, scowly left eye. In short he looks like an angry old git, which is generally how he is drawn within the charmless and largely masculine circle of British political cartoonists. Writing as another bearded old git at the wrong end of his seventh decade, I feel entirely justified in depicting him in that way without risking any charge of ageism. Where I diverge from my colleagues, at least in the mainstream press, is in my attitude to his politics. That's why I try not to draw him in a Lenin cap with a red star on it.

MI6 certainly thinks he is a tool of the Kremlin, and clearly has had a file on him for longer than it can remember, though lately it seems to have eluded their attention that Moscow is now a hotbed of gangster capitalism rather than communist subversion. Nonetheless, the former head of MI6, Sir Richard Dearlove, made no bones about denouncing him as a security risk on the front page of the *Daily Telegraph* on the day of the 2017 general election. This was no more than one would expect from the hard-right paper, but such consistent negative attention from the security services gives licence for similar treatment by the BBC, a much more serious problem for him, politically and constitutionally.

What Jeremy Corbyn has done is to successfully challenge the comfortable consensus on the economy. This has been achieved in defiance of a co-ordinated and relentless media campaign to delegitimise and vilify him, aided and abetted by the hysterical and increasingly panicked manoeuvrings of sections of his own party. He has pursued a coherent, consistent and surprisingly polite argument against a policy of savage austerity and has thereby reset the debate on his own terms. Nobody else would have dared do this, especially not with such apparently fatal disadvantages, ranging from his subversive record and his natural scowl to his blatant lack of charisma, oratorical clout or ministerial experience.

But for our purposes this is all still some time in the future. The story of this book begins at the start of 2015, a few months before the general election that paved the way for Corbyn's leadership. On 7 January, twelve people – including five cartoonists – were murdered at the offices of the satirical cartoon magazine *Charlie Hebdo* in Paris by men in black fatigues and balaclavas who violently objected to the way the prophet Mohammed had been caricatured.

ALLAHU AKBAR!

WHY ARE THE FUCKERS STILL LAUGHING AT US?

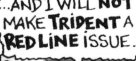

9

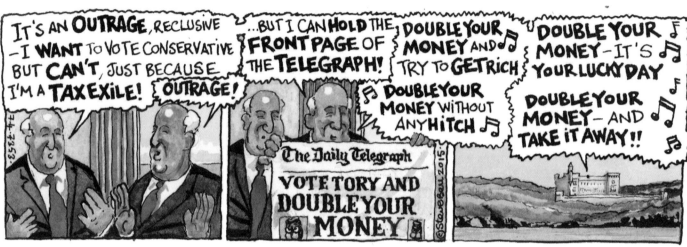

A BETTER PLAN A BETTER FUTURE FOR YOU YOUR FAMILY AND BRITAIN OPPORTUNITY FOR EVERYONE STRONGER FOR SCOTLAND

S o ran the slogans of all four main parties in May 2015, during one of the most dispiriting, negative general election campaigns since the previous one. So bland were they that both Labour and Conservatives managed to share the same deathless phrase 'A Better Future'. In the polls Cameron and Miliband's parties appeared to be running neck and neck, but behind the slogans a fearsome decapitation strategy was at work.

Labour actually made a small percentage gain in England, but was ritually slaughtered by the Scottish National Party in Scotland, losing over forty seats. Nick Clegg's governing Liberal Democrat party was massacred almost everywhere, shrinking from fifty-seven to eight seats overall.

A pumped-up David Cameron managed to win a small overall majority, fighting off a challenge from the UK Independence Party with the promise of a referendum on whether to remain in or leave the European Union. Ed Miliband promptly resigned and the stage was set for further carnage within the Labour party.

17

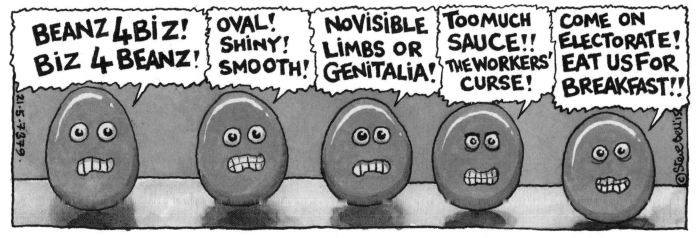

21

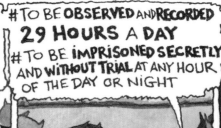

DUCKS, PENGUINS, MONKEYS AND OTHER SOCIAL DETRITUS - GO HOME!

...AND DON'T FORGET TO CELEBRATE WATERLOO!!

after George Cruikshank

I STAND BEFORE YOU...

...THE VANQUISHER OF MILIBONE...

...MASTER OF EUROPE, USHERING IN A CENTURY OF PEACE, PROSPERITY AND BRITISH RIGHTS

I NEED DO NOTHING OTHER THAN PRACTISE MY SNEER OF COLD COMMAND

HIGH'S THE WAR ON POVERTY GOING DUNCAN SMITH?

POOM

ASIDE FROM THE FACT THAT M'HEAD'S BEEN SHOT ORFF...

...IT'S GOING SURPRISING-LY WELL. THE PAUPERS ARE ON THE RUN!!

STAP ME VITALS, DUNCAN SMITH...

...M'RIGHT FLANK'S BEEN OVERRUN BY CHILD PAUPERS!!

I THINK WE FIRST NEED TO CHECK OUR FACTS, YOUR GRACE!

...AS I SUSPECTED! I CAN'T SEE A SINGLE CHILD PAUPER ANYWHERE!

JOB DONE!

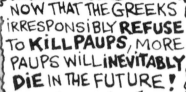

THE LABOUR STAKES HANDICAP

First out of the blocks in the Labour leadership election triggered by Miliband's resignation was the bright-eyed young Blairite, right-of-centrist Liz Kendall. After acting leader Harriet Harman decided not to run herself, the next two to throw their hats in the ring were the left-of-right-of-centrist former Health Secretary Andy Burnham and the right-of-left-of-centrist former Secretary of State for Work and Pensions Yvette Cooper. The would-be candidate of the left, Jeremy Corbyn, was handicapped by his shortfall in nominations from within the overwhelmingly right-of-centre-left parliamentary party. Divine intervention in the form of former Foreign Secretary Margaret Beckett, among others, enabled him to scrape together thirty-six nominations and join the runners. Dame Margaret later implied that she had been a moron to support him.

At this point Harriet Harman intervened to order Labour MPs to abstain on the Tory government's draconian new Welfare Bill. This one act, which Cooper and Burnham as shadow cabinet members were obliged to obey and which Kendall fully supported, prompted a surge in support for Jeremy Corbyn amongst the vast majority of recently enfranchised Labour members who, like Corbyn, opposed the Welfare Bill.

The virulent intervention of former Prime Minister Tony Blair in the campaign did nothing to interrupt Corbyn's progress. The press was in uproar. Political commentators across the entire gamut of British political commentary, from right-of-centre-left to extreme-right-of-beyond-Genghis-Khan, opposed the preposterous rise of the snaggle-toothed elderly bearded terrorist with equal vehemence.

The Kissinger doctrine almost came into play, whereby a recalcitrant and unreasonably left-leaning country needs to be saved from the irresponsibility of its own people (or in this instance membership). Where Chile had needed rescuing from Allende by the divine (US-sponsored) intervention of General Pinochet, a Labour party led by Corbyn would face an immediate coup by at least fifty-seven enthusiastic Blairite MPs from the sensible wing of the party (in this case sponsored by Lord Sainsbury).

Thankfully this never actually came to pass. On 12 September 2015 Jeremy Corbyn was elected leader with 60 per cent of the vote. The coup was to come much later.

©Steve Bell 2015-3.6- 3826-

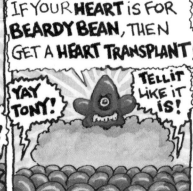

OH FRABJOUS DAY! CALLOOH! CALLAY!

THE COMING OF THE PORK STAR

Having been elected leader, Jeremy Corbyn shortly presented his 'unifying' shadow cabinet, with his long-time ally John McDonnell as shadow Chancellor. A number of MPs, including two rival candidates for the leadership, Yvette Cooper and Liz Kendall, refused to serve under him. Hilary Benn remained as shadow Foreign Secretary and Andy Burnham became shadow Home Secretary.

Since the leader of Her Majesty's Opposition is obliged to become a Privy Counsellor, much was made of Corbyn's historic role as an ongoing threat to the security of the realm – as certified by both MI5 and MI6. Would he or wouldn't he swear the oath of allegiance? Given that he had been obliged to swear a similar oath after

having been elected member of parliament for Islington North eight times, it seemed something of a no-brainer.

However, since media hysteria levels had already been ramped up to eleven, much was made of whether he was prepared to sing the national anthem in public whilst simultaneously moving his lips. While the rest of the country debated these pressing issues, following a modestly successful conference in Brighton under the slogan 'Straightforward Honest Politics', the grassroots campaigning organisation Momentum came into being.

Meanwhile, in Manchester, the Tory party conference was overshadowed by a scurrilous new biography of David Cameron which contained little of note save the saucy 'revelation' that the young Cameron had inserted his member in a dead pig's head as part of an initiation ceremony.

Elsewhere in the universe *The Force Awakens*, a new addition to the Star Wars canon, was widely anticipated . . .

belltoons.co.uk ©Steve Bell 2015· 3909·26·11·15

39

DON'T JUST SIT THERE... BOMB SOMETHING!

TO BOMB OR NOT TO BOMB

In November 2015, 130 people were killed in a dreadful series of terrorist suicide attacks in Paris, eighty-nine of them at a concert in the Bataclan theatre. ISIS claimed responsibility, saying it was a response to French airstrikes on ISIS targets in Syria and Iraq. Condemnation of the attacks along with expressions of solidarity were near universal, but within the Labour party it became an opportunity to express contempt for the perceived pacifism of Jeremy Corbyn with calls for a more muscular and retaliatory bombing campaign.

Bombing somebody in Syria would be an obvious way to build on the rolling success stories in Afghanistan, Iraq and Libya. It would also go some way to make up for the humiliation brought about by Ed Miliband's refusal to lend parliamentary support to similar calls for action against the alleged use of chemical weapons in Syria in August 2013.

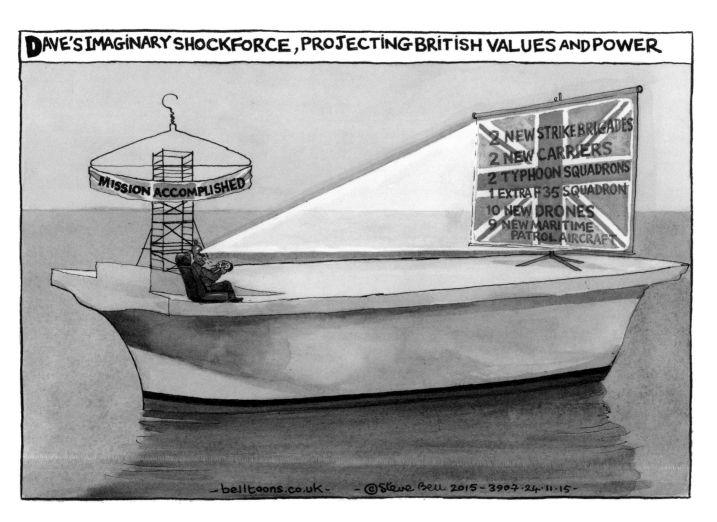

Meanwhile, Chancellor George Osborne was facing an alternative dilemma entirely of his own making. Having in the immediate aftermath of the Tory election triumph made it a legal requirement for the government to balance the books, Osborne was obliged to perform a screeching U-turn in his autumn statement by cancelling a cut to tax credits and thereby breaching his own limits.

Of course, there was plenty of money for extra spending on matters of international security, including the recruitment of new intelligence agents.

And just in case UK politics weren't bleak enough, in the United States Donald Trump, the front-runner to be the Republican candidate for the presidency, announced that:

We need a total and complete shutdown of Muslims entering the United States while we figure out what the hell is going on.

50

PEOPLE OF EARTH – **LORD BUMNOSE** HAS **DELAYED** THE ACTIVATION OF THE ®**PAUPSLAUGHTER**™ BEAM UNTIL 3 WEEKS ON FRIDAY. **JOY TO THE WORLD!**

30·11·7468

IN A GOOD-HUMOURED AND WELL-RECEIVED SPEECH TO THE PEOPLES OF THE EARTH, **LORD BUMNOSE** WILL TODAY REAFFIRM HIS **PLEDGE**...

©Steve Bell 2015

...TO **WIPE OUT POVERTY**, BUILD **400,000 NEW HOMES** AND GUARANTEE A **POLICEMAN** IN EVERY **LIVING ROOM**. THE TERRORIST RENEGADE **JEZ·BIWAN CONORBYN** WAS UNAVAILABLE FOR COMMENT

SQUEEBNORK WE·COME·TO BOMB·SIRIUS BURB SNEEP

YOU'VE **DONE IT** NOW, WATSO·D2!

WELCOME FRIENDLY DROID!...

SQUEEE NORBLE BIP!

©Steve Bell '15

WELCOME TO MY DUNGEON!

NICEWORK, WATSO·D2!

MMMFFF

SQURRRRBLL

NNNFF

AH! ONE'S **REPUB-LICAN GUARD** HAS ARRIVED! WHAT TOOK YOU SO **LONG**?

2·12·7470 ©Steve Bell 2015

WE CAME TO ENGAGE IN GROWN UP AND **RESPONSIBLE TALKS** ABOUT **BOMBING SIRIUS** WITH LORD BUMNOSE

OH NO WE DIDN'T!

OH YES W

IDIOTS!

SQUEE

LORD BUMNOSE HAS **NO INTEREST** IN BOMBING SIRIUS! HE WANTS YOU TO **BOMB EACH OTHER**...

...THEN HE PLANS TO **SHRINK** PLANET EARTH BY **30%**!

WHAT'S THIS **ENIMATED DUSTBIN** THING? WHY IS HE WEARING THIS RIDICULOUS **HET**?

HE'S THE LATEST **D2 DROID**, QUEEN LIZZA!

SQUEE BIP

3·12·7471 ©Steve Bell 2015

CAN HE GET A **MESSAGE** TO SOMEONE WHO CAN **EXTRICATE** US FROM THE **ORDURE**?

NIP NIP· RECORD· MESSAGE· AFTER THE **SQUEEEB**

SUMMONING **KEN SOLO** FROM THE **NEWT PLANET**!!

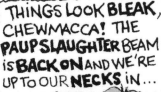

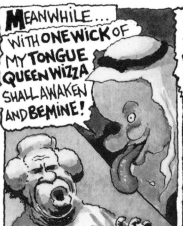

2016

ELSEWHERE, REFERENDUM FEVER TAKES HOLD: 8·2·7500 · ©Steve Bell 2016-

THE PM's CLOTHES

REMAIN ON X

PM's CLOTHES:

LEAVE THEM OFF X

IN A WARMLY RECEIVED SPEECH LATER TODAY, THE PRIME MINISTER WILL ANNOUNCE COMPREHENSIVE PLANS TO REFORM THE PRISONS, DEFEAT WORLD HUNGER...

...AND SHOW THE WORLD HIS ROBUST, SUSTAINABLE AND STYLISH NEW SET OF CLOTHES.

NORMAN THE DOORMAN: YOU'VE SEEN THEM, WHAT ARE THEY LIKE?

WELL, THE FEELING SEEMS TO BE THAT, WITH A BAG OVER YOUR HEAD, THEY'RE ROBUST, SUSTAINABLE AND PRETTY STYLISH

THIS MORNING ON "TOADY" I'M TALKING TO CONORBYNITE SO-CALLED "DEFENCE" SPOKESPATSY, EMILY THORNBERRY, WHO DARES QUESTION THE USE OF "THE WEAPON"

MS THORNBERRY, CAN I INTERRUPT YOU BEFORE YOU START SPEAKING, BECAUSE TIME IS LIMITED...

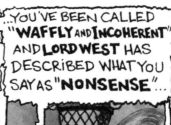

...YOU'VE BEEN CALLED "WAFFLY AND INCOHERENT" AND LORD WEST HAS DESCRIBED WHAT YOU SAY AS "NONSENSE"...

...WHAT WOULD YOU SAY IN RESPONSE TO THAT, ASSUMING OF COURSE THAT YOU HAD ANY TIME TO SAY IT? GOOD MORNING!

WE'VE COME OUT OF THE STUDIO TODAY...

...AND I'M STANDING IN FRONT OF A NOISY PICKET LINE OF JUNIOR DOCTORS WITH A JUNIOR DOCTOR...

...AND A DEAD CAT. TWO QUESTIONS FOR YOU, DOCTOR: ARE YOU GREEDY?

AND: DO YOU FEEL RESPONSIBLE FOR THE DEATH OF THIS CAT?

J'ACCUSE!

61

62

IN A **RAPTUROUSLY RECEIVED BUDGET SPEECH** THIS WEEK, LORD BUMNOSE WILL UNVEIL HIS **BLUEPRINT**...

...FOR **EARTH**, SAFE, SECURE IN AN **EVER-SHRINKING STATE**, FIRMLY **INSIDE** A **REFORMED SOLAR SYSTEM** WITH SOCIAL JUSTICE **FOR ALL**...

... HIS **WEALTHY ASSOCIATES**, AND EVERYONE ELSE **CLEANED OUT** FOR THE **QUEEN**.

...THE **CENTREPIECE** OF LORD BUMNOSE'S HISTORIC **BUDGET**...

...WILL BE A GENEROUS **STARVE-YOURSELF-TO-DEATH-BONUS**, PAYABLE TO **ALL PAUPS** WITHIN **2 YEARS** OF CEASING TO CLAIM BENEFITS...

...A SPOKESMAN FOR THE **BLUE SKIES THINKTANK** WAS SAID TO BE "OVER THE MOON".

CALLING ALL NORTHERN PAUPS! YOU ARE THE NORTHERN POWERHOUSE!! LORD BUMNOSE IS **FIXING YOUR ROOF** WHILE THE **DRIZZLE FALLS**!!!

YOUR ENERGY, AND **ALL** THE PROCEEDS FROM THE '**SAVE-AS-YOU-STARVE**' SCHEME SHALL BE FUNNELED INTO HIS **PORKSTAR**™® OFF-PLANET BANKING FACILITY...

...WHERE IT WILL **GUARANTEE THE FUTURE** OF AN **ENORMOUS HOLE UNDER THE PENNINES**!

EYOOP! WE'RE SAVED!!

AT LAST THE TIME HAS COME TO REMOVE THE **JACKBOOT OF LOCAL DEMOCRACY** FROM **ALL** OUR **SCHOOLS**...

...AND INTRODUCE **FREE** AND **INDEPENDENT** CENTRAL ZOMBIE **BRAIN CONTROL**...

...**DIRECT** FROM THE **PORKSTAR**™® AT A **MODEST COST** OF A FEW **BILLION**!

LORD BUMNOSE is HOLDING A PRESS CONFERENCE

LIVE THE PORKSTAR

I HAVE ABSOLUTELY NO INVOLVEMENT IN, NOR HAVE I EVER, NOR WILL I EVER HAVE DERIVED BENEFIT FROM ANY OFF-PLANET ACTIVITY WHATSOEVER.

LIVE PORKSTAR

THEN WHY ARE YOU SPEAKING TO US LIVE FROM OUTER SPACE?

LIVE PORKST

LOOK! A DEAD CAT!!

LIVE PORKSTAR

IN SENSATIONAL DEVELOPMENTS THIS MORNING, LORD BUMNOSE HAS DISCLOSED, ALONGSIDE HIS SALARY AS A JEDI MASTER, A SMALL INTEREST IN A FAMILY SOFT FURNISHING BUSINESS...

...AS WELL AS SOME RENTAL INCOME FROM A MODEST FLEET OF DEATH STARS. IS HE OFF THE HOOK, NORMAN?...

OR IS THIS CLEAR EVIDENCE OF OFF-PLANET ACTIVITY? WELL NICK, SINCE A DEATH STAR IS TECHNICALLY A SMALL PLANET...

ANY CHARGES OF OFF-PLANET ACTIVITY ARE PRETTY WIDE OF THE MARK!

UNFORTUNATELY QUESTIONS ARE STILL BEING ASKED: HOW CAN LORD BUMNOSE NOT BE INVOLVED IN OFF-PLANET ACTIVITY IF HE LIVES IN A SPACESHIP, AND...

...IF HIS FAMILY SOFT FURNISHING FIRM IS PAYING HIM SUCH LARGE DIVIDENDS...

CAREFUL NORMAN

...THEN WHY HASN'T IT PAID ANY CORPORATION TAX FOR SEVEN YEARS?

I WAS HOPING YOU WEREN'T GOING TO ASK THAT!

WHY DO YOU ENVY THE HIGH ACHIEVER?

UPSTAIRS AT BROADCASTING HOUSE: WHY DO YOU ENVY THE HIGH ACHIEVER?!

I TOLD YOU NOT TO ROCK THE BOAT NORMAN!

UP AGAINST THE WALL BEEB SCUM!! MY MASTER WISHES TO SPEAK WITH YOU!!

I'VE COME TO SECURE YOUR INDEPENDENCE!

AAARRGH! IT'S MR WHITTLASH!

EU REFERENDUM 2016

©Steve Bell 2016 - 3939 · 3 · 2 · 16 -

- belltoons.co.uk

REFERENDUM ON DAVE'S CLOTHES

Having promised an In–Out Referendum on Europe to take place within two years of his unexpected election victory, David Cameron embarked on an intensive, though rather one-sided series of negotiations with our European partners. He had nothing much to offer them, other than a show of toughness aimed to impress his own, largely eurosceptic party and an even more virulently anti-immigrant, anti-EU press pack back home.

In February 2016 Cameron announced that the referendum would take place on 23 June. Six members of his own cabinet opted to back Vote Leave. After a teasing pause, his flexible friend Boris Johnson opted to join them, if only to smooth his own path to the future leadership of the Conservative party.

As Britain prepared to go to the polls, German Chancellor Angela Merkel announced, in the teeth of opposition from members of her own ruling coalition, that Germany was prepared to receive up to a million refugees fleeing the war in Syria. Her neighbours in central and eastern Europe, through whose territory such refugees were obliged to flee, had other ideas.

Within the Labour party, whose leader Jeremy Corbyn commendably refused to play the anti-immigrant numbers game, the knives were already out as members of his own shadow cabinet challenged his perceived lukewarm support for the Remain campaign.

Elsewhere in the news, in the primaries for the US presidential election, Donald Trump was well on the way to winning the required number of delegates to become the Republican candidate for the presidency.

75

77

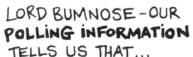

LET'S HEAR IT FOR THE **AUSTRALIAN·STYLE POINTS** SYSTEM

COUNTDOWN TO CHILCOT — GETTING YOUR SPIN IN EARLY

"The price of european holidays has increased" — Official

THE BRITISH PEOPLE SPEAK

But what they said was anyone's guess. As the report of the Chilcot Commission into the war in Iraq drew peacefully to its close, no one was quite sure whether Tony Blair had been castigated as a war criminal or dipped in a bucket of whitewash.

Meanwhile, the referendum campaign undermined the idea that the public opposed immigration as vehemently as UKIP's Nigel Farage. The launch of his poster that suggested that the British people, faced by a flood of suspiciously Middle Eastern-looking migrants, were at breaking point, unintentionally coincided with the vicious murder of Labour MP Jo Cox outside her constituency office by a man shouting 'Britain First!'

People were undoubtedly fed up, but again what they were fed up with was open to any amount of interpretation. As the votes piled up on the night of 23 June it became clear that they wanted out of whatever it was, by a margin of 51.89 per cent to 48.11 per cent.

David Cameron announced his resignation the following morning, though he intended to stand down at the October party conference and hand over to his successor after a civilised campaign within the party to elect his successor. As it turned out he

was gone within three weeks. The campaign of every single candidate except one collapsed in ignominy and Theresa May was triumphantly unelected leader of the Conservative party.

By contrast the Labour party took this opportunity to savage itself, but proved woefully incapable of any such competent ruthlessness. In what became known as the 'Chicken Coup', instigated by shadow Foreign Secretary Hilary Benn and encouraged by deputy leader Tom Watson, the parliamentary party, despite having no obvious candidate or policy goal, passed a motion of no confidence in Jeremy Corbyn.

After various disgraceful attempts to exclude new members from the franchise and Corbyn himself from the ballot paper, the stage was set for a half-baked summer of campaigning by nobody's second choice for leader, Owen Smith, after nobody's first choice, Angela Eagle, pulled out of the contest.

Since Owen Smith seemed to have no clear policy difference with the existing leader other than the fact that he wasn't Jeremy Corbyn, Jeremy Corbyn was re-elected by a second landslide vote, increasing his share from 59.5 per cent the previous year to 61.8 per cent.

83

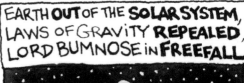

87

89

91

93

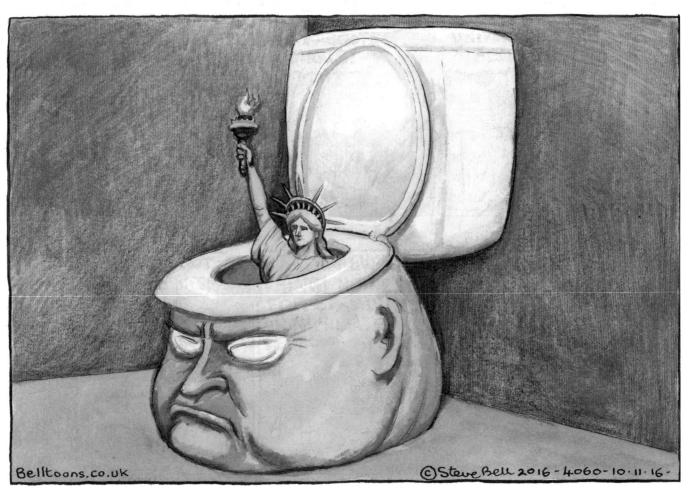

MAKE AMERICA WHITE AGAIN

In an unexpected turn of events Donald Trump was elected to be the oldest, richest, most politically inexperienced and first ever orange president of the United States of America. His victory defied almost every poll prediction, every pundit and every apparent rule of political taste and decency. He had been petulant, contradictory, dishonest, evasive and abusive, despised by many in his own party and openly supported by some of the most flagrantly racist and white supremacist characters in politics, most notably David Duke, former Grand Wizard of the Ku Klux Klan.

Hillary Clinton made a great tactical error by describing such supporters as 'deplorables'. This was taken, understandably but quite dishonestly, to mean his scorned and neglected working-class supporters across the south but also in the so-called 'rust belt' states like Pennsylvania, Michigan and Wisconsin where heavy industry was dying and Trump's message of economic nationalism aimed at protecting American industry was taken very seriously indeed. These states had been assumed to be Democrat certainties, but all went over to Trump. Clinton barely campaigned in these crucial areas until it was too late.

Hillary Clinton won the popular vote by a margin of almost 3 million, yet Trump's insane but focused campaign won him a big majority where it counted – in the electoral college – of 304 to 227. Nigel Farage rushed to Trump Tower in New York to express his delight at the result.

Much was made of Russian interference on Trump's behalf, and subsequent investigations into potential collusion between the Trump campaign and Russian officials were started by the Federal Bureau of Investigation. Then head of the FBI James Comey's own intervention during the last days of the campaign, reviving Hillary Clinton's alleged misuse of personal email accounts for official business some years earlier – which can only have had a detrimental effect on Clinton's support – was curiously overlooked.

In the UK a leaked memo highlighted the fact that the cabinet was hopelessly split on its Brexit negotiating position and had no discernible plan. Furthermore, the inevitable complexities were going to require around thirty thousand extra civil servants. An angry Theresa May reasserted her commitment to the twin mantras 'Brexit means Brexit' and 'No deal is better than a bad deal'. When pressed as to what kind of Brexit she actually wanted, she replied: 'A Red, White and Blue Brexit.' Which clarified things.

LET'S HEAR IT FOR THE RED WHITE AND BLUE BREXIT

SEAL OF THE PRESIDENT OF THE UNITED STATES

E TRUMPIBUS, MAGNUM CACAT

© Steve Bell 2017 · 6 · 1

2017

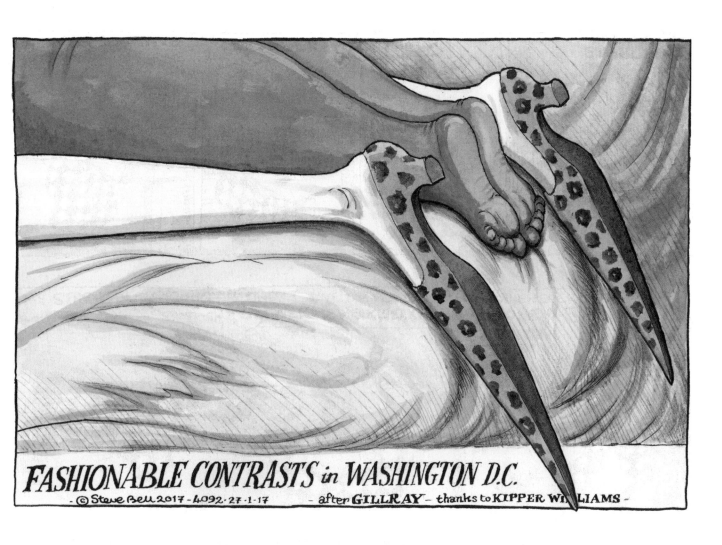

FASHIONABLE CONTRASTS in WASHINGTON D.C.
- © Steve Bell 2017 - 4092 · 27 · 1 · 17   - after GILLRAY - thanks to KIPPER WILLIAMS -

THE SPECIAL RELATIONSHIP

The year got off to an inauspicious start, as Michael Gove was sent to Washington to interview President-elect Trump for *The Times*. Rupert Murdoch was in the room to keep an eye on proceedings. Shortly after this meeting of minds, the inauguration of Donald Trump as forty-fifth president of the United States took place in Washington on 20 January 2017. In attendance his predecessor, George W. Bush, described the inauguration speech, heavy as it was with alt-right conspiracy theory and 'America First' rhetoric, as 'Some weird shit!'

Theresa May led the rush to pay court at the White House when she arrived there a week later and offered the new president a state visit to the United Kingdom. In the Rose Garden she was able to take him by the hand to help him overcome his fear of stairs.

Back home she tried bravely to put flesh on the bones of her pledge to create a Red, White and Blue Brexit, but having established nothing beyond the fact that 'Brexit means Brexit', she resolved to trigger Article 50 of the Lisbon Treaty and did so on 29 March 2017.

This meant that Britain would be gone from the European Union by 29 March 2019, come what may. Since the negotiations on the terms of Britain's departure had so far proved to be chaotic, contradictory and inconclusive, this would provide a secure sense of desperation to underpin any subsequent discussions during the two years that remained.

A media competition for the most frequent use of the words 'Labour party' and 'anti-semitism' in the same sentence reached fever pitch when Ken Livingstone came up for trial before Labour's National Constitutional Committee, not for anti-semitism but for 'bringing the Labour party into disrepute'. The verdict was inconclusive so it was resolved to extend his year-long suspension for a further two years. At the very least it enabled the campaign to continue with renewed vigour.

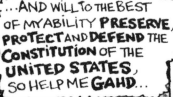

112

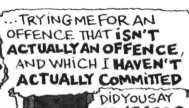

115

· BOZZOLEON'S RETREAT FROM MOSCOW ·

STRONG, STABLE AND CRACKED

There were some remarkable policy U-turns in the air. In the USA President Trump, who had come to power on a pledge to keep out of foreign entanglements, resolved to tackle ISIS in the Middle East by bombing the crap out of a small area of the Achin district of Nangarhar province in eastern Afghanistan. He also announced that a US naval task force was steaming towards North Korea, though it later transpired that it was in fact sailing in the opposite direction.

In the UK, having pledged at least seven times that there would be no snap general election, Theresa May decided to take advantage of her commanding twenty-five-point lead in the opinion polls and announce a snap general election. This was to provide a strong and stable foundation for her position negotiating Britain's imminent exit from the European Union.

Corbyn's Labour party launched its manifesto at Bradford University under the slogan 'For the Many, Not the Few', promising to take back the railways and other public utilities into public ownership, and offering four new bank holidays, a national investment bank and the abolition of student tuition fees.

Having also decided that West Yorkshire was where it was at politically, the Tories launched their programme for continued strong and stable government from a converted mill in Halifax under the slogan 'Forward Together'. They promised to advance the cause of humanity by bringing back grammar schools, reopening the debate on fox-hunting and introducing a hefty tax on people with dementia.

Within a matter of days, the prime minister was forced to perform an embarrassing U-turn on the dementia tax, followed by the declaration that 'Nothing has changed!'

Tony Blair turned sixty-four and confirmed that Theresa May was going to win the election. Meanwhile in France a younger, centrist, rightist heart-throb, Emmanuel Macron, swept to power in the presidential election.

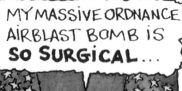

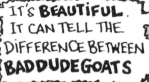

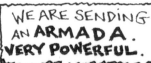

120

I'M NOT SAYING **DON'T VOTE LABOUR**...

...I'M JUST SAYING **THERESA MAY** IS GOING TO WIN...

...AND TO **JEREMY** CORBYN I SAY: "PTHHHRRRPP!!"

...AND IF **THAT'S** BRINGING THE **LABOUR PARTY** INTO DISREPUTE, THEN I'M A **PIECE OF POO!!**

IT WAS **TWENTY YEARS AGO TODAY** RUPERT MURDOCH TAUGHT THE **BAND** TO **PLAY**...

...I'VE BEEN GOING IN AND OUT OF STYLE BUT I'M GUARANTEED TO **RAISE A PILE**...

SO LET ME INTRODUCE **TO YOU**, THE ACT YOU'VE KNOWN FOR ALL THESE YEARS...

...RUPERT MURDOCH'S **THIRD WIFE'S** FAVOURITE MA-A-A-AN!!

WHEN I GET OLDER LOSING MY HAIR TWO WHOLE DAYS FROM NOW...

WILL YOU BE **ACCUSING ME** OF **REAL WAR CRIME**? ARREST WARRANTS, **FORCED TO DO TIME**?

IF I'M **BANGED UP** TILL AGE **NINETY THREE** WOULD YOU **ASK** FOR MORE?

WOULD YOU BELIEVE THAT I'D BE SO GREEDY, **NOW I'M SIXTY FOUR?**

FOR THE BENEFIT OF **MISTER BLAIR** THERE WILL BE A **WAR** SOMEWHERE IN **MIDDLE EAST**

EEEYOWWW!

DAKKA! DAKKA!

THE **MANDELSON** WILL **PRANCE AND SPIN** WHILE **MISTER BLAIR** LIES THROUGH HIS **GRIN WHAT A BEAST**:

MESSRS B AND **M** ASSURE THE **UN DEAD CIVILIANS** SHALL BE **VIRTUALLY NONE**

AND OF COURSE **TROTSKYIST BORES** CALL THESE CLAIMS **FALSE!!**

INFANTS!! THERE'S NO SUCH THING AS A FREE LUNCH!!

...SO YOU'RE NOT HAVING ONE!

A BAD BREAKFAST, ON THE OTHER HAND, IS BETTER THAN NO BREAKFAST AT ALL!!

BECAUSE BREAKFAST MEANS BREAKFAST*

*SHIT SAND-WICH WITH GRUEL OPTION

PARENTS!! JEREMY CORBYN DOESN'T JUST WANT TO STEAL YOUR CHILD'S BREAKFAST...

...HE ACTUALLY WANTS TO KILL YOUR CHILDREN!

ONLY I WILL NOT MAKE A POLITICAL FOOTBALL OUT OF OUR YOUNG POLITICAL FOOTBALLS!!

...ONLY I CAN GIVE OUR YOUNG BRITONS THE BREAKFAST THEY TRULY DESERVE!!

CUT!! CAN WE DO THAT ONE AGAIN?

BREXIT! BREAKFAST! BREAKXIT! BREXFAST!

THERESA MAY RELAUNCH TAKE 35

DON'T LET JEREMY CORBYN SNEAK INTO NUMBER TEN DOWNING ST...

...BY THE EVIL MACHINATION OF DARING TO STAND FOR ELECTION ON A NAKEDLY POSITIVE POLITICAL PLATFORM!

ONLY ONE CANDIDATE IS HONEST ENOUGH TO OFFER THE ELECTORATE A BUCKET OF POISONED FÆCES!

MY CAMPAIGN RELAUNCH IS A RIP-ROARING SUCCESS!

WE ♥ DEMENTIA TAX!

WE 8 FIGURES!

WE DON'T NEED TO KNOW THE FIGURES!

TREAT 'EM MEANER KEEP 'EM KEENER!

MMMMMM WE ♥ POISONED FÆCES!

MMMMM SHE CLEARLY KNOWS WHAT SHE'S DOING!!

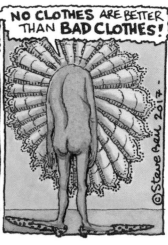

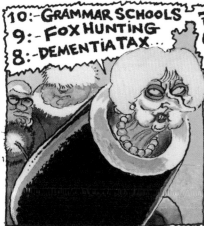

A BURNT-OUT CASE

The last thing anyone expected was for the Tories to lose a twenty-five-point lead and end up with Labour virtually neck and neck. Almost all the polling companies, bar one, called the result wrongly. Nobody, not even the most dewy-eyed optimist on the Labour side, ever saw them gaining thirty seats overall and the Conservatives losing their majority.

A hugely well-funded and relentlessly negative campaign supported by virtually every major news organisation had nearly been defeated by a simple and positive campaign led by a hopelessly unelectable terrorist sympathiser and run by Stalinist henchmen. The sinister anti-democratic stooge of the Kremlin clearly enjoyed campaigning far more than his opposite number.

The Tories were still the largest party and gained twelve seats in Scotland off the Scottish National Party, but now a stunned Theresa May was forced to seek the aid of the Democratic Unionist Party in Northern Ireland in order to form a majority, with a potentially devastating effect on the delicate balance of the peace process there.

The Queen was compelled to interrupt her busy social calendar to open the new parliament with a speech that was embarrassingly short on any new policies. The new May government was unable to deliver on grammar schools or fox-hunting, nor could there be any commitment to anything remotely resembling a dementia tax.

One of the unlikeliest Labour seats narrowly gained was the previously safe Tory stronghold of Kensington. Less than a week later, in the poorer north end of the constituency a terrible fire broke out in a block of flats called Grenfell Tower, in which at least seventy-two people were killed. The block was owned by the Royal Borough and operated at arm's length by the Kensington and Chelsea Tenant Management Organisation.

The fire rapidly took hold and spread up the tower because it had recently been covered in inflammable cladding. Tenants, who had little or no influence over the management organisation, had previously tried to draw attention to the fact that the building was at risk, but had been ignored.

The fire was met with global uproar and disbelief that such a thing could happen in this day and age, and social housing policy over at least the last thirty years was called into question. As of July 2018 the public inquiry is still ongoing.

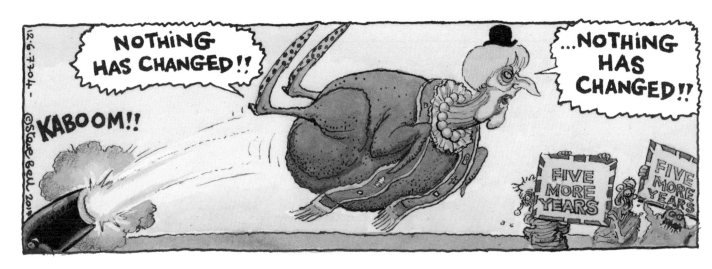

134

RIPPING HISTORY APART

It was while she was on a walking holiday in Snowdonia with her husband Philip that Theresa May had resolved to call a snap election. Three months on from that decision, and after a testing few weeks, she was ready to make another one, in Switzerland, not far from the Dignitas clinic. This time the consequences were less dramatic.

Back in the increasingly rudderless UK, the brand new warship *Queen Elizabeth* – the first of two £3 billion flightless aircraft carriers – was delivered to its new home with the Royal Navy in Portsmouth.

Meanwhile, in an ongoing showdown with North Korean leader Kim Jong Un over his development of a nuclear weapon attached to a missile that could hit the United States, Donald Trump asserted that any such attack 'will be met with fire and fury like the world has never seen'.

In Charlottesville, Virginia a far-right, neo-Nazi rally opposing the removal of a statue of Confederate General Robert E. Lee from a public park was met with a counter-demonstration by civil rights protestors. A car driven into the ranks of the counter-demonstrators by a neo-Nazi supporter killed a young woman, Heather Heyer, and injured twenty others.

In his initial response to the events President Trump refused to directly criticise the white supremacist torch-bearers and laid equal blame on the anti-racist protestors, whom he described as 'alt-left' hate groups. After two days of severe and widespread criticism he eventually issued a rather perfunctory statement that 'Racism is evil'.

Later still he said that he was 'sad' to see America's history and culture 'ripped apart' by efforts to take down the 'beautiful statues and monuments' commemorating the Confederacy.

In Manchester, the stage was set for the Conservative party's annual conference, but not quite as well as had been intended. During an excruciating closing speech Theresa May offered an apology for an election campaign that had been 'too scripted, too presidential'. As she outlined her vision of a 'British dream' a prankster proffered her a giant P45 form. She was also plagued by a persistent cough and accepted a throat sweet from her Chancellor, Philip Hammond. During her long-awaited peroration letters actually started to fall off the conference slogan – BUILDING A COUNTRY THAT WORKS (F)OR EVERYON(E) – immediately behind her.

143

Steve Bell 2017 · 4186 · 2·11·17· — AFTER NAJI AL-ALI — Belltoons.co.uk

THE CLOUD OF UNCERTAINTY

The first anniversary of Donald Trump's election was spoilt when three former campaign managers, advisers and business associates were indicted by Robert Mueller, leading the FBI investigation into possible collusion between the Trump team and the Russians during the 2016 election campaign. One of the three, George Papadopoulos, a former foreign policy adviser, pleaded guilty to lying to FBI agents over contact with people he believed to be senior Russian government officials.

A concurrent anniversary was the centenary of the Balfour Declaration, whereby the British Empire announced support for the establishment of a 'national home for the Jewish people' in Palestine while accepting that 'nothing shall be done which may prejudice the civil and religious rights of existing non-Jewish communities in Palestine, or the rights and political status enjoyed by Jews in any other country.'

This was met with pleasure in Downing Street, where Theresa May entertained Israeli Prime Minister Binyamin Netanyahu; with delight in the White House, where President Trump proclaimed that the US Embassy in Israel would be moving from Tel Aviv to the disputed city of Jerusalem; and with despair and anger in the occupied territories of the West Bank and Gaza.

In Germany, Angela Merkel encountered a setback in her attempts to form a coalition government when the Free Democrats, her traditional partners, walked out of negotiations. In the inconclusive general election of 24 September 2017 her party had lost ground to the far-right Alternative for Germany party. Brexit went even lower down on her list of priorities.

In Britain, Theresa May made much of her new mantra, a 'Bespoke British Brexit deal', but gave little away as to the exact nature or even existence of a large number of assessments of the potential disastrous impact of Brexit on vast swathes of the economy.

Chancellor Philip Hammond in his autumn statement seemed to offer nothing other than a 'Cloud of Uncertainty'.

WITH A **PARADIGM CHANGE**, WHO NEEDS **IMPACT ASSESSMENT?**

154

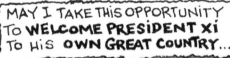

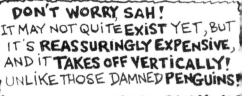

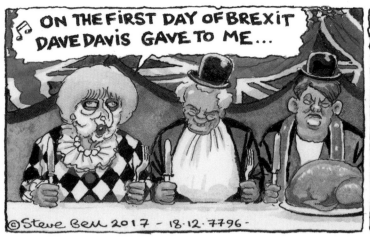

2018

I SPY AGGRESSIVE BEGGARS

A councillor in the Royal Borough of Windsor and Maidenhead, panicked by the thought of potential disruption to the wedding of Prince Harry and Meghan Markle on 19 May, called for a clear-out of people sleeping rough in the Windsor area.

Nearby at Sandhurst in Surrey, at a bilateral summit meeting on security co-operation with France, President Emmanuel Macron presented Prime Minister May with the promise of a loan to the UK of a record of the last successful French invasion, the Bayeux Tapestry.

In other news Carillion, the UK's second largest construction company, went into compulsory liquidation. In the words of the parliamentary inquiry into the collapse it was 'a story of recklessness, hubris and greed' and 'its business model was a relentless dash for cash'. The Private Finance Initiative seemed dead and buried, along with a large number of public infrastructure projects managed by Carillion.

Meanwhile, during a meeting with members of Congress at the White House Donald Trump complained, in reference to immigration from places such as El Salvador, Haiti and certain African nations: 'Why are we having all these people from shithole countries come here?' Never one to trouble himself with consistency, on the first anniversary of his inauguration, in his first State of the Union speech Trump declared: 'If you work hard, believe in yourself, believe in America, you can dream anything.' His apparent attempts before the election to use campaign funds to cover up an alleged relationship with former porn star Stormy Daniels meant that some Americans were starting to dream about his impeachment. Trump himself dreamt of a parade.

B ack in matters of UK politics, on the front page of the *Sun* former Czech intelligence agent Jan Sarkocy named Jeremy Corbyn as a Czech spy with the codename 'COB'. 'Take it from a former spy: the accusations against Jeremy Corbyn should be taken very seriously', raged a *Telegraph* headline, quoting the former head of MI6 Sir Richard Dearlove, the man largely responsible for the vital intelligence underlying the 'dodgy dossier' which was used to justify the invasion of Iraq in 2003.

In response, Ben Bradley MP, the Conservatives' vice-chair in charge of youth engagement, was moved to tweet: 'Corbyn sold British secrets to communist spies.' He felt obliged to delete and apologise for this 'seriously defamatory statement' after legal action was threatened.

In other party news, after a largely unsuccessful Conservative membership drive, the prime minister ordered an away-day brainstorming session at Chequers, her official country residence in Buckinghamshire.

171

THE BEAST FROM THE EAST

As a big freeze out of Siberia struck Great Britain, in the teeth of snowy gales and blasts of criticism of the government's Brexit stance from former Tory Prime Minister John Major, Theresa May delivered another big Brexit speech at the Mansion House. She promised to face 'hard facts' and be 'straight with people' while arguing for two equally improbable alternatives: a 'customs partnership' in which the UK would mirror EU requirements on imports at its borders, and a 'highly streamlined customs arrangement' using technology to minimise 'friction' on the border, later to be known as 'Max Fac', short for 'maximum facilitation'. EU negotiators were equally dismissive of both proposals.

Meanwhile, Emmanuel Macron won the dubious honour of being the first world leader to be invited to Washington by Donald Trump for a state visit. 'I love this guy!' said Trump after a particularly intense physical encounter in front of the cameras at a press conference given by the two leaders.

On 4 March, former Russian intelligence agent Sergei Skripal and his daughter Yulia were found 'slipping in and out of consciousness' in the town centre of Salisbury. They were rushed to the local hospital by the emergency services, where they were assessed as having been affected by an unknown substance. The UK government later confirmed that the pair had been poisoned by a nerve agent so pure, so

powerful and so obscure that it had to be 'novichok', which could only have been delivered by a government agency, most likely Russian.

Many questions, most notably who exactly, what exactly, where exactly, when exactly and most importantly why exactly, remained unanswered. The Russians emphatically denied any responsibility. There was, however, a series of tit-for-tat diplomatic expulsions and a further cooling of the already frozen relationship between the UK and Russia. The Skripals, originally thought almost certain fatalities, have now recovered and are safe and sound at a secure location somewhere in the UK.

After a meeting of the Commonwealth heads of government, almost certainly the last to be hosted by Her Majesty the Queen, a delegation of leaders asked to meet Theresa May. On the agenda was to be a discussion of the fate of a number of long-term residents of the UK who had been summarily thrown out of the country as part of the Home Office's 'hostile environment' for illegal immigrants. Since all of the people in question were entirely legal residents and citizens who had lived here since childhood, the request was at first dismissed.

However, the story of the mistreatment of the 'Windrush generation', named after the ship that brought thousands of West Indian immigrants to work in Britain in 1948, would not go away – not least thanks to a long-running investigation by Amelia Gentleman in the *Guardian*. It cost Home Secretary Amber Rudd her job and raised questions about the successful author of the 'hostile environment' policy, one Theresa Mary May.

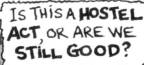

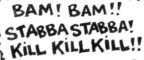

MY LORDS, AT THIS TIME OF YEAR I FEEL IT IS INCUMBENT ON ME TO RAISE...

...THE THORNY ISSUE OF THOUSANDS OF CHIFF CHAFFS THAT COME OVER HERE; THAT EAT OUR FLIES...

SHAME!

...THEY SING THEIR MONOTONOUS SONGS THEY USE OUR HEALTH SERVICE...

POINT OF ORDER!

CAN YOU GIVE ONE RECORDED INSTANCE OF A CHIFF CHAFF EVER HAVING USED THE HEALTH SERVICE?

THAT'S BESIDE THE POINT... ...MY LORDS...

CHIFF CHAFF CHIFF CHAFF CHIFF CHAFF

OI! YOU!!

HAVE YOU COME FROM AFRICA?

NAH MATE I WAS HATCHED IN WANDSWORTH

HAVE YOU SPENT EXTENDED PERIODS OUTSIDE THE UK?

WHY DO YOU WANT TO KNOW?

I NEED TO KNOW WHETHER TO GET HOSTILE ON YOUR ASS OR NOT

I'M A WOOD WARBLER!

THIS ISN'T ABOUT LEGAL MIGRANTS...

LEGAL MIGRANTS HAVE MADE AN ENORMOUS CONTRIBUTION TO OUR COUNTRY...

AND LOOK! .... FABULOUS BODY ARMOUR FOR ME!!

THE FACT OF THE MATTER IS THAT THE BRITISH PEOPLE ARE OVER-WHELMINGLY IN FAVOUR...

...OF CREATING A HOSTILE ENVIRONMENT FOR ILLEGAL MIGRANTS

CHIFF CHAFFS GO HOME

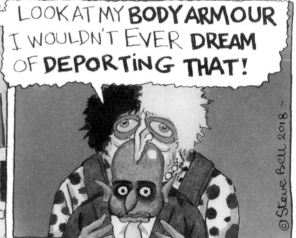

LOOK AT MY BODY ARMOUR I WOULDN'T EVER DREAM OF DEPORTING THAT!

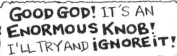

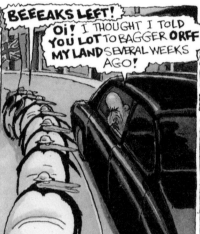

© Steve Bell 2018·7·4 - AFTER HOLMAN HUNT -

THE SCAPEGOAT

A year on from her surprise election non-triumph and despite being a 'dead woman walking', Theresa May is still bouncing from U-turn to U-turn, still devoid of any original policy, other than a belated borrowing of much of Ed Miliband's 2015 manifesto, still without a position or a policy on Brexit, still dependent on the whims of the DUP and still, miraculously, in office.

Jeremy Corbyn seems to have recovered from his brief respite from near-universal opprobrium and returned to his natural status as pariah – at least in the eyes of the popular press and his cohort of critics on the Labour benches, though that is a good deal smaller than it was. The same authoritative commentators in the columns of the same quality papers are still explaining to him what he must do to appease that cohort and avoid being wiped out at the next election, and he is still, mercifully, ignoring them.

And the goat shall bear upon him all their iniquities
unto a land not inhabited:
And he shall let go the goat in the wilderness.